ISBN-13: 978-17320527-2-7

Bear Lake ABCs

M is for monster, who lives in the lake

by KD Brown

especially for mom and dad

I love you

**is for aquamarine,
the color of the lake**

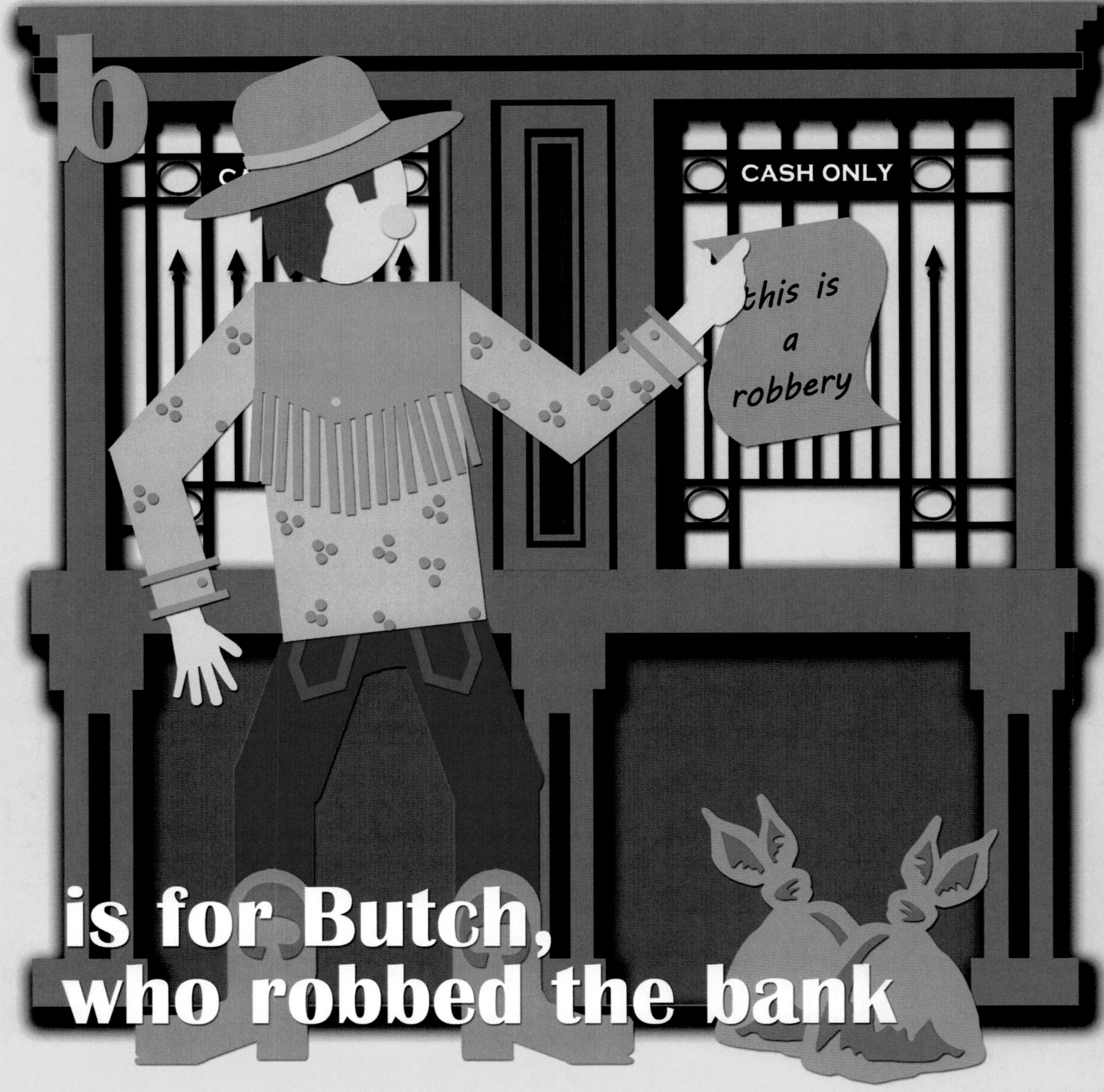

b is for Butch,
who robbed the bank

is for Cisco, a fish you catch when it's cold

d is for deer, who graze
in the meadow

e

is for elk, who graze there too

f is for fun with friends & family, gathered around the fire

g is for gulls, who steal your food on the beach

h is for huckleberries
that take ages to pick

is for ice caves that are fun to explore

j

**is for
jacket that you
wear when it's windy**

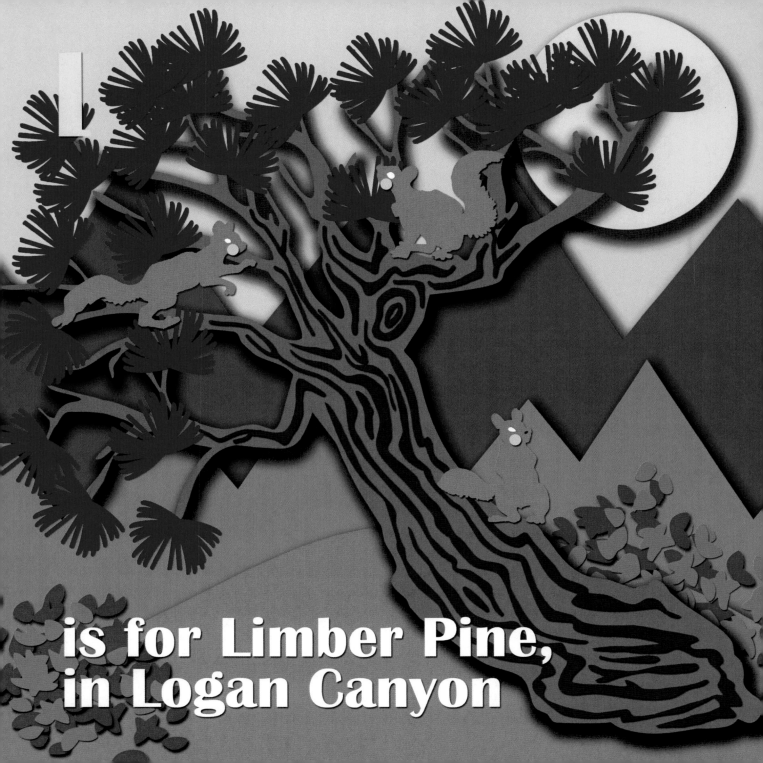

L is for Limber Pine,
in Logan Canyon

m is for monster, who lives in the lake

n

is for nighttime out under the stars

is for Oregon Trail that runs through the West

q is for quaking aspen, rustling in the breeze

r is for rope swing
at Bloomington Lake

t is for toes that peek out from your tent

u is for
underground cavern
in Minnetonka Cave

V is for the Vir-Day, a family-run motel & cafe

W is for

world-famous
milkshakes
from Garden City

X

ABC
DEFG
HIJKL
MNOPQ
RSTUVW
XYZ

is for x-ray at the doctor in Montpelier

y is for yellow-headed blackbird, who lives in the marsh

About the Author

The author lives in Idaho with her long-suffering husband, Tyson, and their loyal dog, Lily.

KD loves reading, sometimes writing (mostly the procrastination of it), and occasionally even drawing. Growing up, she spent her summers picking raspberries in Garden City and swimming at North Beach.

This is her first picture book.

Lily, also called Pig or Piggy, is a Vizsla. She loves running, chasing squirrels in Fish Haven, and eating spoils that fall on the kitchen floor.

Lily dog also makes a cameo in *B is for Buffalo*, a picture book showcasing the fun of Yellowstone National Park from A - Z.

Follow **@whatkatydrewnext** on Instagram & Facebook to see what KD, Lily, and Tyson are doing next.

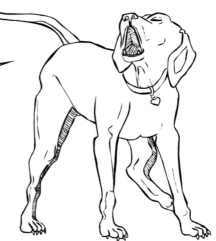

If you enjoyed this book, please take a moment and leave an honest review on Amazon.com (or wherever you purchased this book). It's a great way to help independent authors.

Made in the USA
Middletown, DE
06 August 2024